BUILD A PIRATE
AND OTHER
LEGO® ACTIVITIES

Pick an activity...

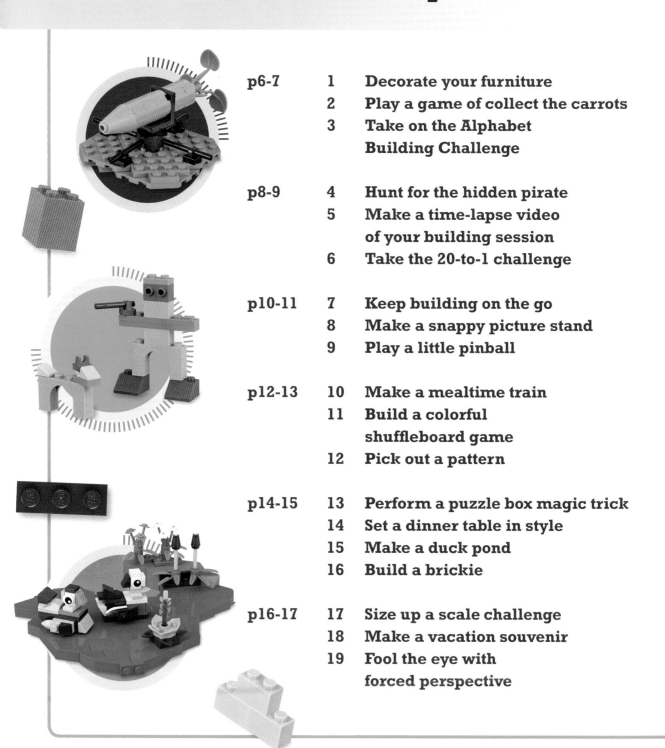

p6-7
1 Decorate your furniture
2 Play a game of collect the carrots
3 Take on the Alphabet Building Challenge

p8-9
4 Hunt for the hidden pirate
5 Make a time-lapse video of your building session
6 Take the 20-to-1 challenge

p10-11
7 Keep building on the go
8 Make a snappy picture stand
9 Play a little pinball

p12-13
10 Make a mealtime train
11 Build a colorful shuffleboard game
12 Pick out a pattern

p14-15
13 Perform a puzzle box magic trick
14 Set a dinner table in style
15 Make a duck pond
16 Build a brickie

p16-17
17 Size up a scale challenge
18 Make a vacation souvenir
19 Fool the eye with forced perspective

p18-19   20   **Make some numbers**

21   **Build a book cover**

22   **Hold an award ceremony**

p20-21   23   **Make a working sundial**

24   **Build a ship in a bottle**

25   **Put the head on the minifigure**

26   **Guess the minifigure**

p22-23   27   **Keep your kitchen tidy**

28   **Make a beautiful stained-glass window**

29   **Sort at speed!**

p24-25   30   **Build your own zoo**

31   **Make a sign that shines**

32   **Play the ball-in-the-hole game**

p26-27   33   **Make a picture-perfect easel**

34   **Build a coaster puzzle**

p28-29   35   **Make a micro-scale set**

36   **Play a game of peg solitaire**

37   **Build a charm for your bag**

p30   **Acknowledgments**

1 Decorate your furniture

Building around table legs is a fun way to liven up parts of furniture that often go unnoticed. Surprise visitors by decorating the legs on your dining table, desk, or even bed! Add minifigures to a simple square shape or try building different patterns.

Most table legs are not very exciting!

Stack alternating bricks from both connecting walls to create strong corners

AN IDEA WITH LEGS

Make sure your decoration fits the table leg perfectly by building on site. Begin by creating a frame of thin plates around the leg and then start stacking. If you prefer, try leaving a gap in your build so that it can slot on and off the table leg without you having to take apart your model.

Can you collect more carrots than your rival rabbit? Find out with this bunny-based board game. Hop from square to square in search of a sprouting snack, but watch out for the prickly thorns! A carrot spinner decides which way your bunny bounces, but you decide how far it can move! This board is big enough for two players but you could build a larger one if you have more players.

> A BIG STEP FOR A MINIFIGURE!

Build around your table leg, but not underneath it.

Single-color stairs allow colorful minifigures to stand out

2

3 Take on the Alphabet Building Challenge

Slope bricks create a curved handle shape

Comb, cat, crayon, or car could all be good "C" builds

Comb teeth are thin bar pieces

The Alphabet Building Challenge is as easy as A, B, C! Give your friend a letter from the alphabet and 30 seconds to pick an object to build that begins with that letter. Let them choose a letter for you, decide on an object, and race to create your chosen builds.

RULES OF THE FIELD

Place an odd number of carrots and a few obstacles on your board before you play. Space them out and change their position in between games. Make sure that both players are sitting on the same side of the board as the carrot spinner, so that you both agree which way is up!

Carrot connects to an angle plate and spins on a turntable

A LEGO® Technic axle connects the carrot parts

A bunny on top of a 1x1 round plate creates a playing piece

Thorns are fixed to plates with top clips

HOW TO PLAY

1 Each player places their rabbit on the board, on a square of their choice.

2 Take turns spinning the carrot. See which way it points: up, down, left, or right.

3 Move any number of squares you wish in that direction. If you land on a square with a carrot top—collect the piece!

4 You cannot land on or pass over squares with thorns, so you must wait for your next turn to go around them.

5 When all the carrot tops have been picked, the winner is the player who has collected the most!

Dark-green squares create a grid on the light-green base plate

Carrot shoots fit into flowers with holes

Bars separate the spinner sections

Decide which section is up, down, left, and right

Play a game of collect the carrots

4

Hunt for the hidden pirate

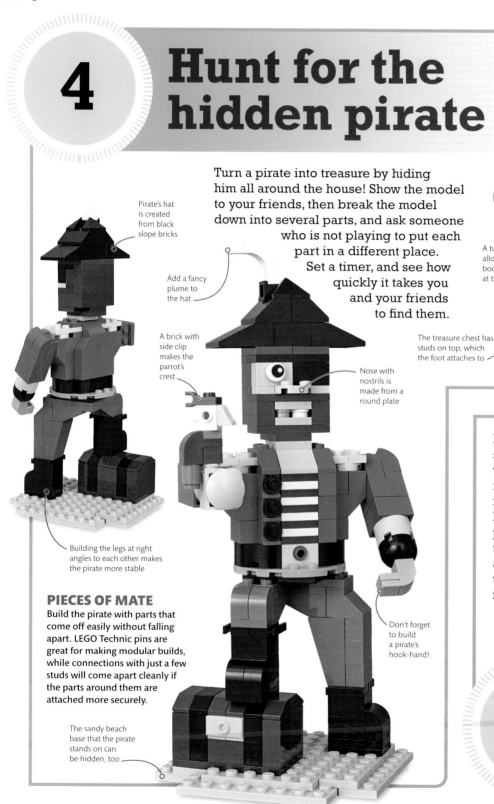

Turn a pirate into treasure by hiding him all around the house! Show the model to your friends, then break the model down into several parts, and ask someone who is not playing to put each part in a different place. Set a timer, and see how quickly it takes you and your friends to find them.

The pirate breaks down into six parts to be hidden

A turntable allows the body to twist at the waist

Pirate's hat is created from black slope bricks

Add a fancy plume to the hat

A brick with side clip makes the parrot's crest

Nose with nostrils is made from a round plate

The treasure chest has studs on top, which the foot attaches to

Building the legs at right angles to each other makes the pirate more stable

PIECES OF MATE
Build the pirate with parts that come off easily without falling apart. LEGO Technic pins are great for making modular builds, while connections with just a few studs will come apart cleanly if the parts around them are attached more securely.

Don't forget to build a pirate's hook-hand!

The sandy beach base that the pirate stands on can be hidden, too

Play back your building session as it happened with a cool time-lapse movie! Take photos at regular intervals as you build, and record the process from beginning to end. Play the pictures as a movie or slideshow to see your model made in a matter of seconds!

5

Take the 20-to-1 challenge

6

Take 10 pairs of matching bricks and see what you can build using all of them. Then take one brick away and build something completely different with the 19 pieces you have left. Keep rebuilding with one brick fewer every time. How close can you get to making 20 different things?

A house and backyard can be built out of only 11 pieces

This castle gate with guards uses all 20 pieces

Small slopes become the guards' helmets

This man and his dog are made from just 18 pieces

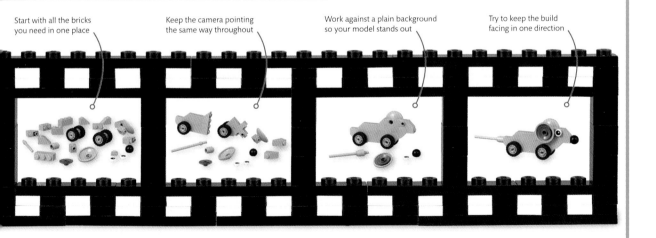

Start with all the bricks you need in one place

Keep the camera pointing the same way throughout

Work against a plain background so your model stands out

Try to keep the build facing in one direction

Make a time-lapse video of your building session

7

Keep building on the go

Make your journeys go faster by taking a LEGO® travel pack with you. All you need is a box with a secure lid, a choice selection of bricks, and some homemade challenge cards to choose from. To make it harder, build against the clock!

Keep your builds relatively small and simple

A handful of bricks can connect in hundreds of different ways

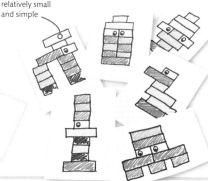

Use your bricks to recreate the models on your cards.

Take two of each brick you need, so you can play with a friend

If you want to show off your photos in style, why not make a LEGO picture stand? This one has a simple clip that snaps shut to hold a photograph without damaging it.

The entire stand is built sideways

A broad base keeps it stable

Leave this space for the hinge

The clip opens at the hinge— the rubber band closes it

Make a snappy picture stand

8

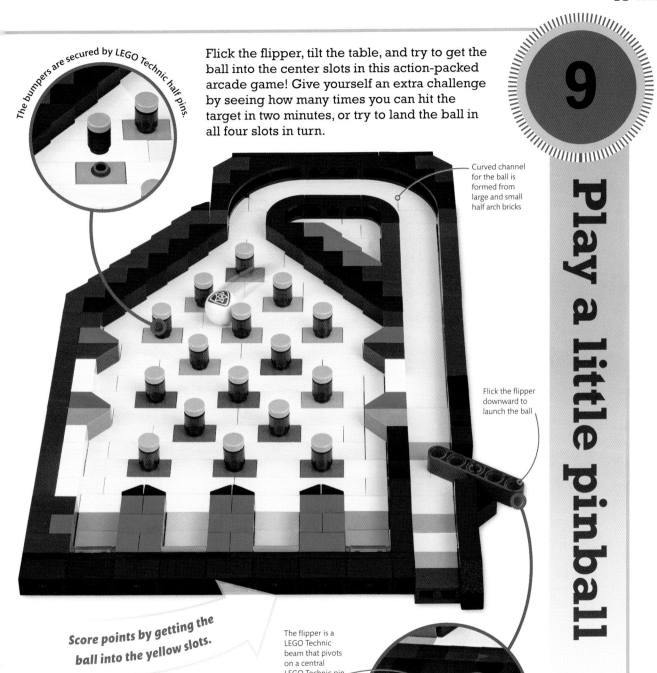

The bumpers are secured by LEGO Technic half pins.

Flick the flipper, tilt the table, and try to get the ball into the center slots in this action-packed arcade game! Give yourself an extra challenge by seeing how many times you can hit the target in two minutes, or try to land the ball in all four slots in turn.

Curved channel for the ball is formed from large and small half arch bricks

Flick the flipper downward to launch the ball

Score points by getting the ball into the yellow slots.

The flipper is a LEGO Technic beam that pivots on a central LEGO Technic pin

9

Play a little pinball

A GAME OF TWO LAYERS
The pinball table is built sideways with just two layers of bricks, each one-stud deep. The bottom layer is mostly white and flat, but with some colored bricks extending upward to form part of the top layer. All the curves and slopes are on the top layer only, except for the slopes on the outside edges.

Make a mealtime train

All aboard! This train is bound for all destinations around the dinner table, calling at cutlery, condiments, napkins, and serving spoons! It makes a great decoration when set up on a track around the middle of a table, and you could even add an electric motor!

Train buffers connect with magnetic couplings

Numbers are built into the sides of the cars using small black bricks and plates

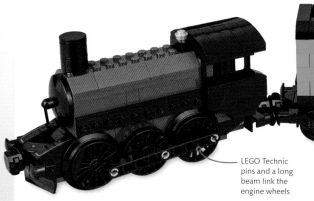

LEGO Technic pins and a long beam link the engine wheels

Train car wheels turn on bogie plates

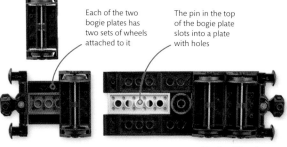

Each of the two bogie plates has two sets of wheels attached to it

The pin in the top of the bogie plate slots into a plate with holes

Underside of car

FULL STEAM AHEAD

Even if you don't have train wheels and tracks, you can still build a LEGO train! Large automobile wheels without their tires and even LEGO Technic gears can make train wheels that run without a track, while smooth tiles or plates with rails can be used to construct straight lengths of track.

THE SPECIAL BRICK

Bogie plates are 4x6 pieces with a pin on top that let train wheels turn with bends in the track.

HOW TO PLAY

1 The first player places one piece at the flat end of the board, slightly overhanging the edge, and flicks it once along the board.

2 The same player repeats this with four more pieces, leaving each piece where it lands.

3 The player scores one point for each piece that lands on a different color and is not on a white line.

4 The pieces are collected up, and the next player begins their turn following the steps above. The winner is the player with the highest score after three turns each.

Both cars can hold items to be passed around the table

A red light indicates which end is the back of the car

12 Pick out a pattern

Look around, you'll see patterns everywhere—on walls, floors, clothes, and pillows! Look at how they repeat colors and shapes, then invent a new pattern using the techniques you have seen.

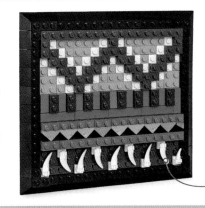

This tartan pattern looks the same whichever way you turn it

This Aztec pattern uses claw pieces to make curves

This game is easy to learn, but harder than it looks to master! Players slide their playing pieces along the board, trying to get them all into different colored sections. Landing on a color scores a point—but landing on a white line scores nothing at all!

Use curved pieces to create the end barrier

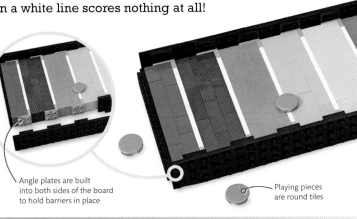

Barriers stop the playing pieces from coming off the board

Angle plates are built into both sides of the board to hold barriers in place

Playing pieces are round tiles

BUILDING THE BOARD

The shuffleboard is built as a high brick wall and laid on its side for playing the game. Building a smaller board or dividing it into fewer sections makes the game easier to play, but not so exciting to watch!

Build a colorful shuffleboard game

13

Perform a puzzle box magic trick

WHAT'S IN THE BOX?

The secret is two LEGO Technic axles on the small box, which slot into bricks with holes in the bigger box when the puzzle is tilted a certain way. This makes the two boxes lock together—until they are tilted back the other way!

Each axle fits inside two layers of bricks with holes

A third layer of bricks stops the axles from sliding in the wrong direction

When the boxes are tilted downward, the axles slide into these bricks with holes, locking the boxes together

The orange squares show which end of each box is the locking part

Line up the orange corners when putting the small box back inside

The handle is made from corner panel pieces

The axles slide in and out as the boxes are tilted

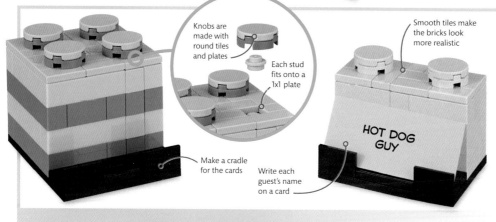

Knobs are made with round tiles and plates

Each stud fits onto a 1x1 plate

Smooth tiles make the bricks look more realistic

There is no need to guess who is coming to dinner when you use these stylish place card holders! Each one is shaped like a giant LEGO brick, with a stand at the front for a name.

Make a cradle for the cards

Write each guest's name on a card

HOT DOG GUY

Set a dinner table in style

14

maze your friends and
amily with this mystifying
uzzle box! Hand it over
with the orange corners
lting downward and no
ne will be able to lift the
maller box out of the big
ne. Take it back with the
range corners upward and
ne magic boxes will slide
part with ease! You could
ven set a timer and see
who can solve it in the
hortest amount of time.

I NEED TO THINK INSIDE THE BOX!

Make a duck pond

15

Create a water feature for your home without getting wet! It is easy to build a pond or puddle shape. Then all you need to do is add animals and plants to make a cute scene.

Bulrushes are made from cones and bars

The water is built sideways using slope bricks

The lily is built upside down, starting with a plate with a pin

Build a brickie

16

It takes a second to take a selfie, but how quickly can you build a brickie? Challenge your friends to make LEGO self-portraits in 10 minutes and then compare your funny faces!

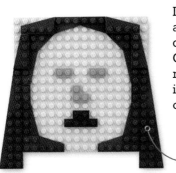

Build a simple brickie with plates of different sizes

Different slopes make a realistic hairstyle on this more detailed brickie—this version would take longer than 10 minutes!

Facial features are attached to bricks with side studs

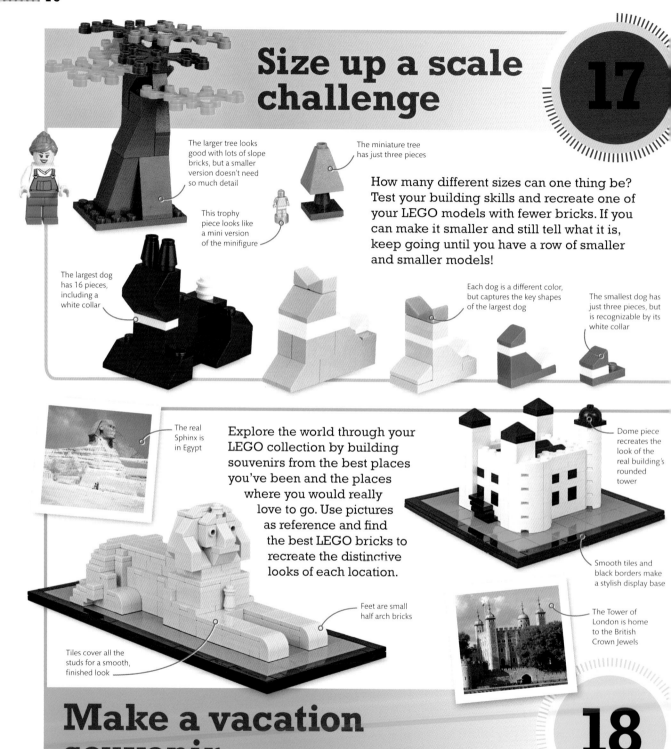

Size up a scale challenge

17

The larger tree looks good with lots of slope bricks, but a smaller version doesn't need so much detail

The miniature tree has just three pieces

This trophy piece looks like a mini version of the minifigure

How many different sizes can one thing be? Test your building skills and recreate one of your LEGO models with fewer bricks. If you can make it smaller and still tell what it is, keep going until you have a row of smaller and smaller models!

The largest dog has 16 pieces, including a white collar

Each dog is a different color, but captures the key shapes of the largest dog

The smallest dog has just three pieces, but is recognizable by its white collar

The real Sphinx is in Egypt

Explore the world through your LEGO collection by building souvenirs from the best places you've been and the places where you would really love to go. Use pictures as reference and find the best LEGO bricks to recreate the distinctive looks of each location.

Dome piece recreates the look of the real building's rounded tower

Smooth tiles and black borders make a stylish display base

Feet are small half arch bricks

Tiles cover all the studs for a smooth, finished look

The Tower of London is home to the British Crown Jewels

Make a vacation souvenir

18

19 Fool the eye with forced perspective

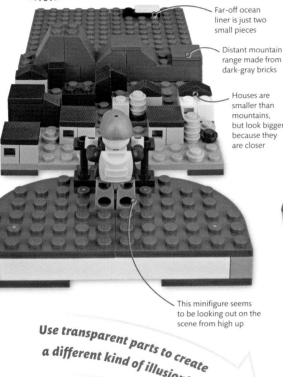

Far-off ocean liner is just two small pieces

Distant mountain range made from dark-gray bricks

Houses are smaller than mountains, but look bigger because they are closer

This minifigure seems to be looking out on the scene from high up

Make your builds look much bigger than they really are—by making some of the parts smaller! Forced perspective is a way to create a sense of depth by putting larger things in the foreground, and smaller things farther away. The eye treats all the objects as if they are the same scale, so it assumes that the small things must be very far away!

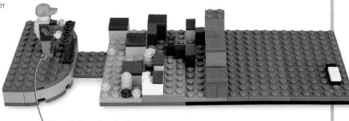

The minifigure is actually only one brick higher than the scene!

PHOTO FINISH

Forced perspective scenes only work when seen from the right direction, which means they can look especially good when photographed with care. Take photos of your forced perspective builds from their best angles—and you could turn them into a gallery of your greatest optical illusions!

BUILDER'S TIP

Place minifigures in the foreground of your forced perspective scenes for an instant sense of scale.

Use transparent parts to create a different kind of illusion!

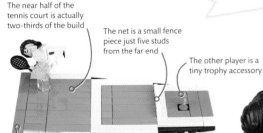

The near half of the tennis court is actually two-thirds of the build

The net is a small fence piece just five studs from the far end

The other player is a tiny trophy accessory

The build is much wider at this end than the other end

This minifigure is leaping for the ball

A small round plate is the tennis ball in mid-air

The player on the far side of the net looks very far away

20 Make some numbers

From lucky numbers to birthdays, some numbers are always worth remembering. Rather than simply writing them down, though, you could build them instead! You can display them to mark significant dates, use them to remember important numbers, or mix them up to make math puzzles!

These numbers run through a rainbow of colors

Brick-built numbers can lay flat or stand up on a base plate

A good book paints a picture in your mind, so why not build those pictures out of LEGO bricks! Take your favorite book and think about what you would put on its cover—it should give people an idea of what the story is about. Build it in 3-D for a challenge, or make your cover flat using a base plate.

You could make up your own book—this one is about a New York cab driver!

21 Build a book cover

The 3-D effect is achieved by attaching pieces to bricks that are sticking out of the background

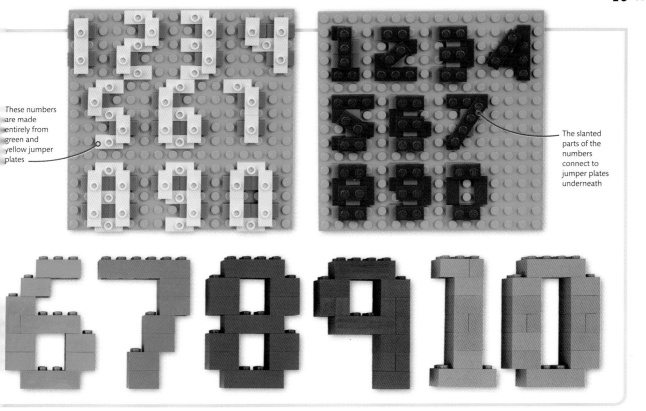

These numbers are made entirely from green and yellow jumper plates

The slanted parts of the numbers connect to jumper plates underneath

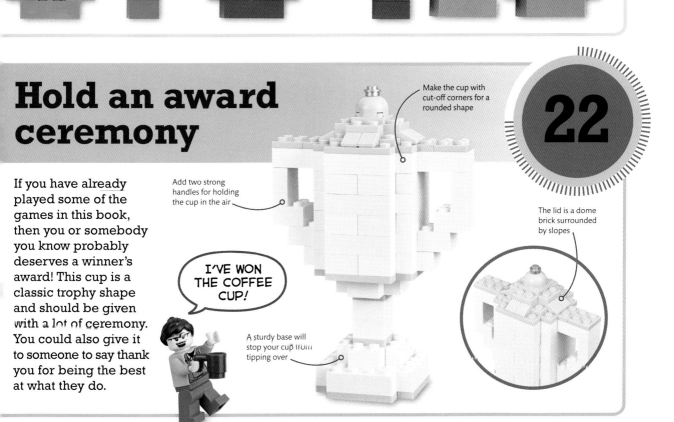

Hold an award ceremony

If you have already played some of the games in this book, then you or somebody you know probably deserves a winner's award! This cup is a classic trophy shape and should be given with a lot of ceremony. You could also give it to someone to say thank you for being the best at what they do.

Make the cup with cut-off corners for a rounded shape

Add two strong handles for holding the cup in the air

The lid is a dome brick surrounded by slopes

22

I'VE WON THE COFFEE CUP!

A sturdy base will stop your cup from tipping over

23 Make a working sundial

Tell the time with a LEGO sundial. It looks like a normal clock but with a pointer at 12 o'clock. Place in the sunshine at the start of an hour, and line up the shadow to the right time. Come back throughout the day for regular time checks!

The shadow will be here when it is 11 o'clock

This marker will be in the shade at 3 o'clock

This long shadow shows that it is just after 5 o'clock

IT'S PAST 5 O'CLOCK— TIME FOR A SNACK!

Look for a bottle with a neck big enough for the hull, but too small for it to fit with raised sails

These sails fold forward

The hull is just three studs wide

SETTING SAIL

To fit the ship inside the bottle, build it with sails fixed to clips so they can fold forward or to the side. With the sails folded down, the ship should fit through the neck of the bottle. Once it is inside, use a stick to gently nudge the sails into an upright position.

Fold this sail to the side first

Bars on the sails attach to clips on the deck

How does this LEGO ship fit inside the bottle? It looks impossible, but the secret is in the sails! Sailors have been making ships in bottles for hundreds of years. No self-respecting pirate would be without one!

Stand is made from upside-down half arch bricks

24 Build a ship in a bottle

25 Put the head on the minifigure

Give a classic party game a LEGO twist by trying to pin the head on a minifigure! Players take turns wearing a blindfold and try to place the head. It is sure to make you laugh your head off!

LEGO Technic half pins poke through for the eyes to attach to on the other side

Sideways headlight brick allows you to attach the head to the board

THE SPECIAL BRICK

Use angled plates to create interesting shapes. Two 2x4 angled plates form each of the minifigure's arms.

The body includes a long neck stud, just like a real minifigure

Pick minifigures with distinctive parts

Can you identify minifigures just by how they feel? Place 10 minifigures inside a fabric bag and give your friends one minute each to feel the minifigures through the bag. The winner is the player who guesses the most minifigures correctly!

26 Guess the minifigure

Plates creating the minifigure shape and white background attach to two base plates underneath

A STUDY IN STUDS
The body is built with studs facing out so that the head can be attached anywhere. The background can be as big as you like, but the larger you make it, the more likely it is that blindfolded players will attach the head in completely the wrong place!

Keep your kitchen tidy

Build taller compartments for your longest utensils

Add tiles on top for a smooth finish

The base is made from two plates

ONE TABLESPOON OF FLOUR... THAT'S GOING TO BE HEAVY!

PERFECTING THE RECIPE

Design your utensil holder in colors to match the kitchen it will go in. Before you start to build, ask permission to borrow some safe utensils so you can see how big and tall it needs to be. If all the utensils are roughly the same size, make it with just one large compartment.

27

Make room for big utensils in even the smallest kitchen with this useful storage solution. It has four sections at different heights to hold longer and shorter items, and small holes at the bottom to stop crumbs from gathering inside. Any budding chef would be glad to get it as a gift!

The shape of this window is made by half arch bricks on both sides of the transparent bricks

Clear transparent plates alternate with colored transparent bricks

Add colorful light effects to your LEGO buildings by giving them stained-glass windows! There are lots of ways to do this using different transparent bricks and interesting lattice pieces. The best effects mix several colors at once. Hold your finished windows up to the light to see them really glow!

28

Sort at speed!

29

For this game, every player has a cup full of random bricks. Decide how to sort the bricks—by color, size, or brick type. The first player to sort all of their bricks is the winner! To make the game fair, swap your cups of random bricks after every go. Why not time yourselves and start a sorting leader board?

Put your mixed bricks into three cups for sorting

These bricks have been sorted by brick type

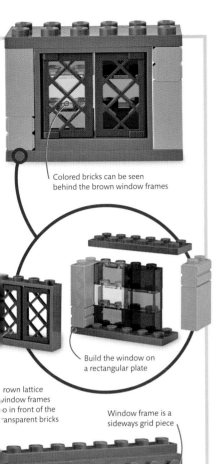

Colored bricks can be seen behind the brown window frames

Build the window on a rectangular plate

rown lattice
indow frames
o in front of the
ransparent bricks

Window frame is a sideways grid piece

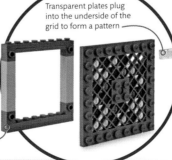

Transparent plates plug into the underside of the grid to form a pattern

The grid fits onto bricks with side studs so that it can be built into a bigger wall

LET THERE BE LIGHT
If you make a building with a stained-glass window, leave the back wall open so light can shine through it from behind. Or build a LEGO light brick into the structure to give a warm glow that will bring the whole building to life.

Make a beautiful stained-glass window

30 Build your own zoo

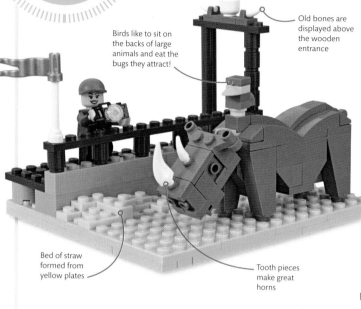

Birds like to sit on the backs of large animals and eat the bugs they attract!

Old bones are displayed above the wooden entrance

Bed of straw formed from yellow plates

Tooth pieces make great horns

WATCH THE WILDLIFE

Think about how big the animals should be alongside minifigures. Make use of unusually shaped pieces and sideways building to create realistic, characterful creatures. Add hinge pieces to create movement and natural-looking angles, such as the tilted head of the rhino.

Only the zookeeper is allowed on this side of the barrier!

The penguin's eyes are side studs

A penguin's head with no body looks like it is underwater!

Find out more online or in books about how animals like to live, then decide what to include in each enclosure.

Go wild with models of all your favorite animals in your very own LEGO zoo. Think about the conditions they like to live in and build an enclosure for each animal. Why not ask your friends to build their own favorites and then bring them all together in one big wildlife park!

Gorilla's ears are bricks with side studs

Shoulders are half arch pieces

EEK!

Brown round plates make droppings!

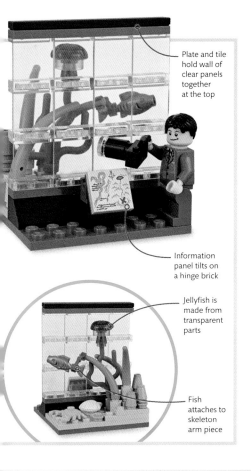

Plate and tile hold wall of clear panels together at the top

Information panel tilts on a hinge brick

Jellyfish is made from transparent parts

Fish attaches to skeleton arm piece

Play the ball-in-the-hole game

32

Get all five balls into their color-coded holes—just by tilting the box. For an even tougher challenge, try doing it against the clock!

Circular elements from LEGO® NINJAGO® sets

Balls run smoothly on tiles

Build the sides high enough to stop the balls from rolling out.

Begin with a square base plate

Use your transparent pieces in a different way to make neon signs. Build a picture using transparent pieces and black pieces only. Position your finished sign in front of a flashlight to see it shine!

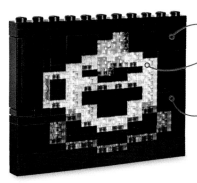

Picture is one-stud deep

Transparent plates form the shape of a coffee cup and saucer

Black bricks will really make the colors stand out

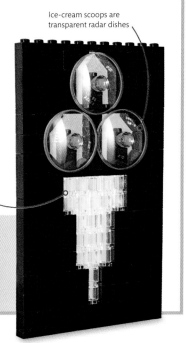

Ice-cream scoops are transparent radar dishes

Ice-cream cone is made from transparent round bricks

31

Make a sign that shines

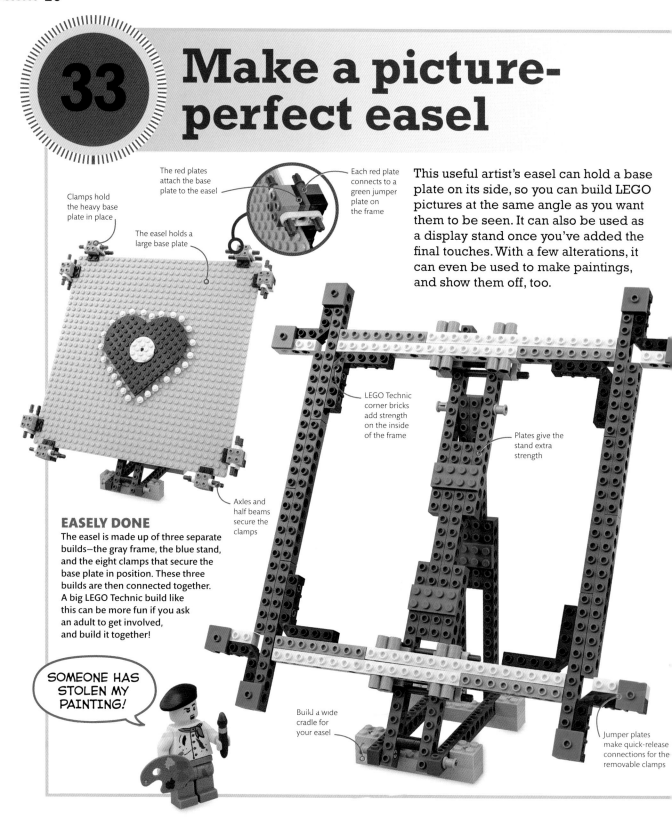

33 Make a picture-perfect easel

This useful artist's easel can hold a base plate on its side, so you can build LEGO pictures at the same angle as you want them to be seen. It can also be used as a display stand once you've added the final touches. With a few alterations, it can even be used to make paintings, and show them off, too.

The red plates attach the base plate to the easel

Each red plate connects to a green jumper plate on the frame

Clamps hold the heavy base plate in place

The easel holds a large base plate

LEGO Technic corner bricks add strength on the inside of the frame

Plates give the stand extra strength

Axles and half beams secure the clamps

EASELY DONE
The easel is made up of three separate builds—the gray frame, the blue stand, and the eight clamps that secure the base plate in position. These three builds are then connected together. A big LEGO Technic build like this can be more fun if you ask an adult to get involved, and build it together!

SOMEONE HAS STOLEN MY PAINTING!

Build a wide cradle for your easel

Jumper plates make quick-release connections for the removable clamps

Build a coaster puzzle

34

This puzzle doesn't take too long to solve, and when it is done, it becomes a cool-looking drinks coaster! Set a timer to see how quickly you can solve it, then match up the pieces so that no two tiles of the same color touch. Reward yourself with a cold drink and a stylish pattern to rest it on!

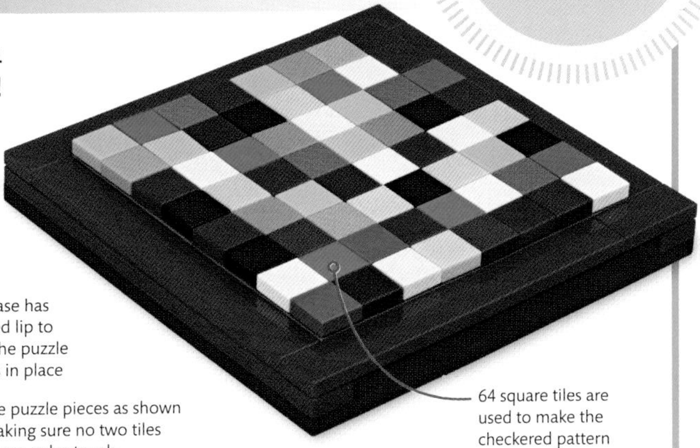

Use corner plates to make the edge pieces

The base has a raised lip to hold the puzzle pieces in place

Build the puzzle pieces as shown here, making sure no two tiles of the same color touch

64 square tiles are used to make the checkered pattern

THE SPECIAL BRICK

Crossblocks are very useful LEGO Technic connectors that link elements in two different directions.

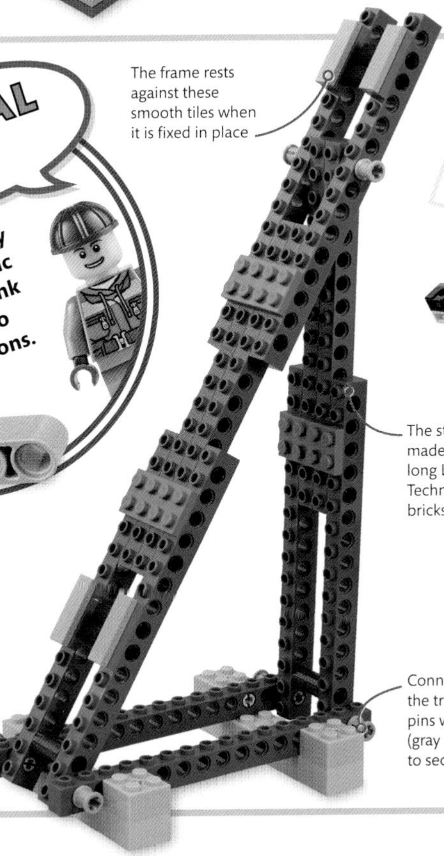

The frame rests against these smooth tiles when it is fixed in place

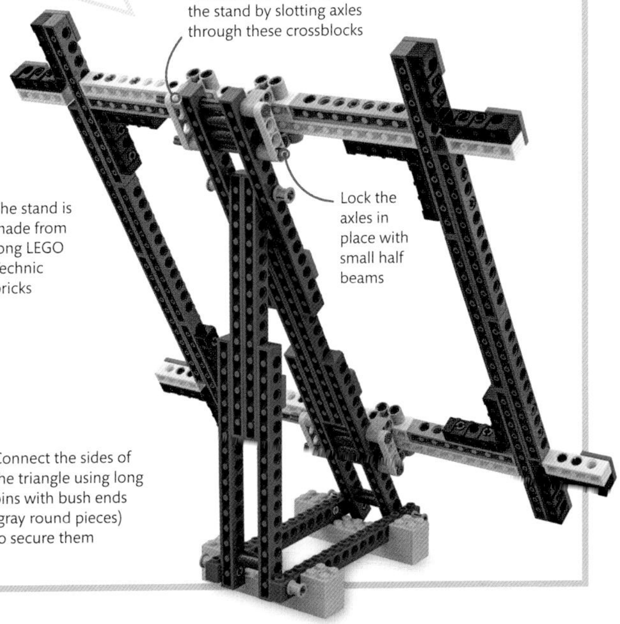

You can adjust the angle of the stand by moving where these top pins connect.

Connect the frame to the stand by slotting axles through these crossblocks

The stand is made from long LEGO Technic bricks

Lock the axles in place with small half beams

MAKING A STAND

The stand that supports the easel frame is built as a large triangle, held together with LEGO Technic pins. The frame is securely attached to the stand, and the whole thing stands on a wide base to keep from tipping over.

Connect the sides of the triangle using long pins with bush ends (gray round pieces) to secure them

Make a micro-scale set

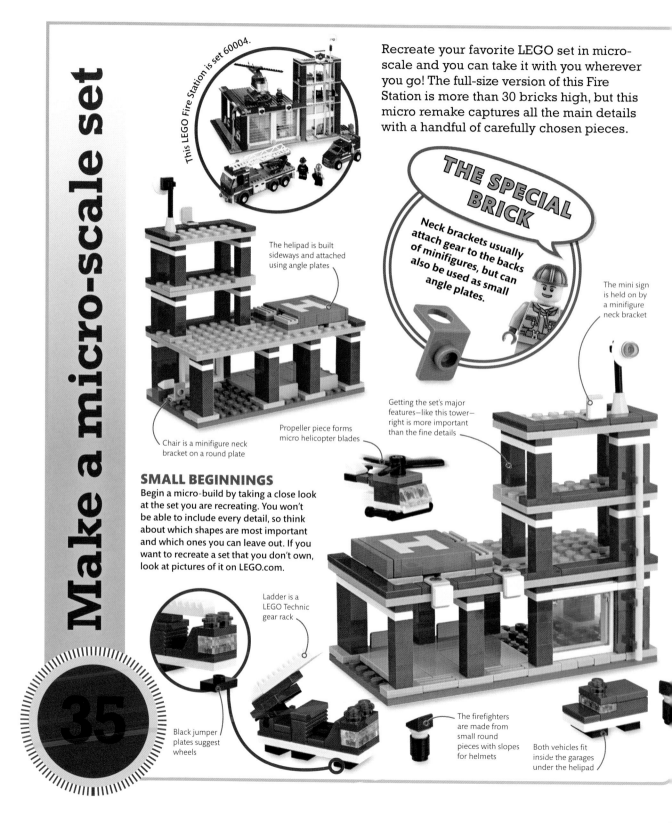

This LEGO Fire Station is set 60004.

Recreate your favorite LEGO set in micro-scale and you can take it with you wherever you go! The full-size version of this Fire Station is more than 30 bricks high, but this micro remake captures all the main details with a handful of carefully chosen pieces.

THE SPECIAL BRICK

Neck brackets usually attach gear to the backs of minifigures, but can also be used as small angle plates.

The helipad is built sideways and attached using angle plates

The mini sign is held on by a minifigure neck bracket

Getting the set's major features—like this tower—right is more important than the fine details

Chair is a minifigure neck bracket on a round plate

Propeller piece forms micro helicopter blades

SMALL BEGINNINGS

Begin a micro-build by taking a close look at the set you are recreating. You won't be able to include every detail, so think about which shapes are most important and which ones you can leave out. If you want to recreate a set that you don't own, look at pictures of it on LEGO.com.

Ladder is a LEGO Technic gear rack

35

Black jumper plates suggest wheels

The firefighters are made from small round pieces with slopes for helmets

Both vehicles fit inside the garages under the helipad

Play a game of peg solitaire

36

Plunge into a game of strategy and skill with this classic one-player puzzle. Whether you build a round board or a square one, there is no way to cut corners—you need to make the right moves right from the start!

32 small round bricks for playing pieces

The base is made from four curved bricks

Alternating plates form a cross-shaped grid

The pegs are spaced out so that they are easy to grasp

Use these spaces to store pegs removed from the board

HOW TO PLAY

1 Start with 32 pegs—one on every square except the center one. Move one peg at a time by jumping it over another peg into a vacant square (your first move will be into the center square).

2 Pegs can jump in any direction except diagonally, and you can only jump over one peg at a time. Every time a peg moves, the peg that it jumps over is removed from the board.

3 The object of the game is to move the pegs in a sequence that leaves no peg stranded in a position where it cannot jump over another. You win the game when there is just one peg left on the board. Once you've solved it, try playing against the clock for an even tougher challenge!

Smooth tiles look like a wall of multicolored LEGO bricks

Chain connects to built-in plates with bars

Studs make this charm look like a classic LEGO brick

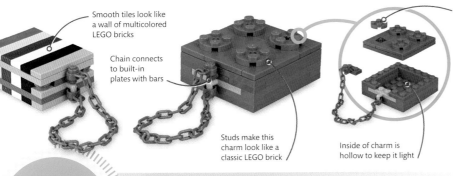

Each 2x2 round plate attaches to a 1x1 plate surrounded by smooth tiles

Inside of charm is hollow to keep it light

Use a LEGO chain piece to add a unique charm to your favorite bag or backpack. These charms look like giant LEGO bricks, but you can make yours look like anything!

37 # Build a charm for your bag

Senior Editor Helen Murray
Senior Designer Jo Connor
Editors Pamela Afram and Matt Jones
Designers Ellie Boultwood, Rhys Thomas, and Thelma Robb
Additonal editors Beth Davies, David Fentiman,
and Laura Palosuo
Pre-Production Producer Kavita Varma
Senior Producer Lloyd Robertson
Managing Editor Paula Regan
Design Managers Jo Connor, Guy Harvey
Creative Manager Sarah Harland
Publisher Julie Ferris
Art Director Lisa Lanzarini
Publishing Director Simon Beecroft

Models built by Joshua Berry, Jason Briscoe, Stuart Crawshaw, Naomi Farr,
Alice Finch, Rod Gillies, Kevin Hall, Barney Main, and Drew Maughan
Photography by Gary Ombler

Dorling Kindersley would like to thank Randi Sørensen, Paul Hansford, Martin Leighton Lindhardt,
Henk van der Does, Lisbeth Finnemann Skrumsager, Michael Madsen, and Jens Rasmussen
at the LEGO Group. Thanks also to Julia March at DK for editorial assistance and
Sam Bartlett for design assistance.

Picture credits: p16 (l): Peter Wilson © Dorling Kindersley;
p16 (r) Max Alexander © Dorling Kindersley.

First American Edition, 2017
Published in the United States by DK Publishing
345 Hudson Street, New York, New York 10014
DK, a Division of Penguin Random House LLC

Contains content previously published in *365 Things to do with LEGO® Bricks* (2016)

Page design copyright © 2017 Dorling Kindersley Limited

001-308350-July'17

A catalog record for this book is available from the Library of Congress.

ISBN: 978-5-0010-1484-3

Printed in Heshan, China

www.LEGO.com
www.dk.com

A WORLD OF IDEAS:
SEE ALL THERE IS TO KNOW